Highland Cattle Galor

Gu leoir, Gaelic for *sufficient*, in English became galore m

By Ùna F Cochrane

Master Jack Craig of Craig Auctioneers, Ayr & Newton Stewart, demonstrates the docility of a Highland Bullock in 1900.

An early advertisement from the Dewhurst chain of butchershops which moved into retailing meat from Argentine and New Zealand, having pioneered refrigerated shipping by the 1880s. In Fort William, Lochaber, Dewhurst's Eastman outlet was known in the 1930s as "the frozen meat shop".

Acknowledgements

During the collecting of material for this book friendly co-operation, inspiring goodwill and help came from ever cheerful postcard dealers, Highland Cattle breeders, archivists, artists, photographers and copyright holders. Special thanks to Jen Gillan for use of the late Tom McLatchie's photos and to Alastair White for photographs and post-cards; to The Highland Cattle Society, Dr.E King, A MacPhail, J Headon, J P Ramsay, J A MacMaster, J Clarke, E A Cameron, G Hobhouse, W A T Wisely, G Macpherson, N and G Stacy-Marks, L Jack, S Clapp, A MacFarlane, L Genever; to Erica J Cochrane for rapid typing of draft texts, to Ian Cochrane for postcard searches from Andover to Aberdeen and wizardry with a wayward computer, and to the delightful Stenlake Publishing team.

PREFACE

This book celebrates a breed of domestic cattle that evolved alongside the flourishing of ancient man in the once forested shores, glens and mountains of Scotland. Truly indigenous, Highland Cattle have special attributes used today in projects re-establishing a healthy range of bio diversity in wide country spaces.

Now to be found happily munching in many other countries – Canada, France, New Zealand, Holland, the United States of America, Finland, Germany, Belgium, Australia, Switzerland, Denmark, Poland, Norway, Austria, Sweden, Luxemburg, the Faroe Islands, and the Czech Republic, Highland Cattle were for many centuries in the ancient past most probably the only cattle throughout Scotland apart from the now extinct fierce, large, truly wild forest breed called Urus or Auroch. Over long expanses of time different types of cattle arrived in the British Isles, and intermingled both naturally and by human design until breeds "as various as the soil of the different districts or the fancies of the breeders" (W. Youatt) were fixed and recognisable. Few of these new breeds adapted economically to the harsh environment of western, northern, island and high land Scotland. In the agriculturally progressive Scotland of 1834, there were still no other cattle than the Highland breed in the Gaelic speaking Hebrides, but their numbers, like the Gaelic language with which they are historically linked, were steadily diminishing. Thanks to a century of dedicated private enthusiasts Highland Cattle have not joined the ranks of endangered species.

The breed today remains essentially the original type, having escaped the fervour of the breed-changing "improving" schemes so prolific in the early days of agricultural science. The distinctive long haired and horned appearance attracts attention now, as it did in the Edwardian heyday of picture postcards. Postcards, though of less commercial and social importance in an information technology age, continue to offer images of the breed, noticeably in glowing well-fed health unlike the hungry animals recorded by adventuring photographers of the early 20th century. Highland Cattle were, however, moving closer to being a bygone species at that time than many realise, and their future is still far from guaranteed.

Photographer Pharmacist D Macpherson introduced his young Edinburgh cousin to Highland Cattle on her first visit to Kyle of Lochalsh by asking her to sit as a milkmaid for this picture, taken circa 1915. Today a new medical practice stands on the land behind where the bemused cow is in this scene. *Reproduced by kind permission of the photographer's daughter, the late Mrs Mary Hudson, "Glenquithel".*

Breed Attributes

The iconic charisma of Highland Cattle dispels the attitude that 'cattle are cattle, all the same, four legs, bulgy udders, chomp grass, look stupid.' Always photogenic, they are far from stupid as they quietly assess you looking at them. No other British cattle have both long hair and long horns. Their four athletic short legs will take them over fences and through rivers whenever they want. They chomp far more than grass – apples and twigs from your garden are more of a treat than shrubby heather, birch or willow. They find raw potatoes irresistable, and woollen socks hanging out to dry make a tasty snack if within reach. The first Swiss farmer to import Highland Cattle called them débrousailleuses, the eat everything cattle. They can reason independantly as well as with group instinct. Cows and bulls live beyond 18 years before retiral – often to parks in Visitor Centres. Discreetly tucked under their long outer coat the cows have tidy little udders designed to feed one calf with very rich creamy milk. Each calf stays with its mother until young adulthood at six to nine months. Calves grow to full maturity in separate grazings. Surplus animals later supply the beef trade with a supremely tasty low cholesterol meat of singular quality. Like the Powan of Loch Lomond, the Red Squirrel, the wild Pink Primrose and the Scottish Crossbill, they are native to Scotland and not yet extinct like the Fife and the Buchan cattle which were among those lost in changes effected by the 18th century agricultural revolution.

© UFC

Highland Cattle have an important function beyond supplying beef or looking picturesque. Hardy and less genetically altered by man than most other British domestic cattle breeds, they are better able to thrive in rough hill grazings exposed to the unpredictable Scottish elements. Because the breed has a large gut specially adapted to digest tough plants and grasses, they work wonders in restoring biodiversity to areas ravaged by years of overgrazing from too many sheep and deer, which relentlessly nibble away the fine herbage and sapling trees leaving the rough stuff to grow rampant and dominate. This restorative attribute, along with the fact that they need neither housing nor specialised veterinary care when calving, has made them a welcome part of the management policy of nature reserves in Britain and Europe.

In general Highland Cattle are not naturally aggressive towards people. The important exception to the usual easy-going docility of Highland Cattle is the cow with calf. Predatory foxes, wolves, bears, and incautious pet dogs quickly learn how fiercely protective she is and how dangerous her horns are if provoked. Should she wrongly associate a human moving near her calf with her fear of a predator, she is likely to charge with intent to heave the two-legged intruder out of her calf zone. Cows from many breeds are prone to attack strangers who may stray too close to the calf, and in all breeds there can occur a bad tempered individual, but Highland cows were hand milked in the open with their calf free beside them - this skill is still practised by a North Uist breeder – and more old reports can be traced of milkmaid injuries from Ayrshire cows horns than from Highland.

4

Cows demonstrate well the 'individual look' of Highland Cattle fully within the standards set by pedigree regulations. Horn and hair, head, body shape and size, bone and leg length can differ noticeably.

Mother and Son

© T.McLatchie

5

The individual look in bulls, yet all share the same breed characteristics of hardiness, longevity, docility when managed appropriately, and a specialised ability to convert tough herbage into usefulness.

A HIGHLANDER.

"Beneath a craggy steep"

Sparse grazings – a lot of mountainside is needed to support this hardy breed on the poor quality grasses, heather and rushes of these regions. In this circa 1906 photo, behind the white, not albino, Highland calf is the bull, central as is usual in his fold (for fold see page 46).

The Glasgow born artist Joseph Denovan Adam (1842 – 1896) had a keen interest in Highland Cattle and shows here some bullocks in the natural coat colours of the breed (from left, dun, white, red, black, yellow, with possibly a brindle extreme right). His works featuring them as the main subject were unsurpassed. At his Craigmill Art School, Stirling, in the 1880s, he kept a small fold and would walk fearlessly among them. The public could study " these hornymental animals without being tossed" quipped the magazine Punch about Adam's London exhibition in 1890. Under the enthusiastic direction of Dr Elspeth King, the Stirling Smith Art Gallery and Museum, which owns five Adam originals, ran a splendid centenary exhibition of his work in 1996. The Stirling Smith Art Gallery opened in 1874, ten years before the Highland Cattle Society was formed.

Quiet natured Highland bullocks are such practical and photogenic assets to many policies open to the public today that they can enjoy 22 or more years of leisure instead of joining the beef-provider herds, or working as their forebears did pulling carts and ploughs.

Courtesy of T. Scott May

"Jock" at Douglas Castle.

9

For these Highland bullocks in good summer grazings in Lanton, Northumberland, theirs was a shorter journey from "snowy Doune" November sales than those bought there for Yorkshire and East Anglian destinations.

This postcard of Lanton sent with an Alnwick postmark dated 1907, reads 'This is the farmhouse here and Kyloes. Got all our potatoes up, and a good crop.'

Highland Cattle can endure blizzards and temperatures dropping to minus 40 degrees because of their thick hide and double layered coat. They will search out any natural wind break such as trees. Yorkshire landscape painter F.W Hulme (1816 – 1884) here ably presents Highland bullocks in snow.

Above: One of HRH King Edward VII's own Highland bullocks in 1909.

Below: On their way to their Birkhall residence in the 1940s two kindly persons with deep knowledge of the countryside and rural affairs, HRH King George VI, Patron of the Highland Cattle Society of Scotland until 1952, and Queen Elizabeth. Their daughter, the present Queen, continues her father's patronage of the society and maintains a quality fold of Highland Cattle at Balmoral Castle.

Above: In this sketch by R M Paxton for The Sphere newspaper in 1900 these splendid Highland bullocks at the Smithfield Show, London, 1900, catch the attention of the Prince of Wales (later King Edward VII), who was popularly regarded as a 'friend of the farmer' and who was an active president of the Highland and Agricultural Society of Scotland for a year.

The current Royal family are regular attenders at agricultural shows, throughout Britain. In her tour of The Royal Highland Show, in 2000, HRH The Princess Royal included the Highland Cattle judging ring in her itinery. While not represented below the Queen's Balmoral Fold of Highland Cattle achieve notable successes in show and sales rings.

© UFC

A Quiet Feature of Tourism

A Highland cow takes time to identify the carter and his load progressing up the hill, in case they herald the arrival of a tasty meal. Uig, Isle of Skye, in 1912 had yet to experience roads busy with tourism to Scotland, so bustlingly vibrant in the Loch Lomond area, popularised by Victorians when travel abroad had become politically dangerous.

Left: Thomas Cook tours to Inversnaid were successfully operating as early as the 1850s. Hugely fashionable circular tours in The Trossachs from the 1860s to the 1930s used well integrated travel by rail, steamer and horse-drawn coach. Popular romantic novels set in real locations in the area drew crowds keen to visit them and the home territory of the outlawed cattle drover Robert (Macgregor) Campbell, laird of Inversnaid, better kown as Rob Roy. However, the Inversnaid to Stronachlachar horse-drawn coach service seen here finally closed in 1937. Highland Cattle still graze near Inversnaid and around Loch Lomond. *Left*: The region around The Trossachs (rough or bristly hills, or from na troiseachan: hills cut by a pass) was a mecca for 19th century tourists. They could steam sail up Loch Katrine (Ceiteirein: loch of the furies) to Stronachlachar Pier (place of the stonemasons) and transfer to a horse-drawn open-air coach bound for Loch Lomond's Inversnaid pier and take a ferry across that loch, or a steamer trip down it to the railhead at Balloch.

Courtesy of Alastair White

Right: These Highland cows with day old calves are in Strathyre in the heart of Rob Roy country. Cows with young calves will square up to unknown intruders with enough ferocity to protect their young. Rob's men, and the imposters seeking to blame him for their own thieving exploits, would have known that, but it is no longer common knowledge in today's largely urbanised society.

Laggan Farm, Strathyre

The long waterway of Loch Awe, with the dramatic Kilchurn Castle ruins at the east end, was and remains a much visited location. Highland Cattle have retained a presence around Loch Awe seemingly for centuries, although in many areas they disappeared when the Highlanders left their homelands. The total number of cattle in the crofting counties fell by more than two thirds between 1800 and 1855. The delightful annual agricultural show at nearby Dalmally, which boasts a fine auction mart and railway station, usually attracts a good presence of Highland cattle. Tourists in the early twenty-first century no longer have the choice of pleasure boat sailings that once plied Loch Awe.

The Ardnamurchan peninsula (*right*) and the Hebridean Machair Lands (*below*) supported more cattle than visitors in the 1930s. Now fewer Highland Cattle are seen by greater numbers of visitors. Crofts are discernable in the background of the Ardnamurchan view which is near Port nan Spainndeach: Bay of the Spaniards, so named after an encounter there between Scots and Spaniards in 1588.

courtesy of J. Headon

An example of a parti–colour Highland cow (ringed),in the first few years of the twentieth century, at home on Iona. Transport of livestock to and from the islands is easiest with young stock. But that means long term planning is a vital element of island life, when one considers that purchase of a yearling heifer means feeding and looking after her for another three years before she will deliver a new calf and yield milk.

GAIRLOCH HOTEL, GAIRLOCH

The growth of tourism created a demand for hotels. Gairloch Hotel (gearr: short loch) erected in 1872 with grounds and hothouses for its own supply of grapes, flowers, vegetables and eggs, was enlarged in 1881. Until the mid 20th century such hotels kept a few dairy cows to supply fresh cream, milk, and sour milk for scones, pancakes and baking. The presence of the cattle no doubt endorsed for tourists the authenticity of the highland destination. Sometimes Highland Cattle were shipped from Stornoway markets direct to the Gairloch area which held local cattle markets twice annually.

The Scottish poet farmer Robert Burns is credited with composing 'The Birks o' Aberfeldy' when he visited the Falls of Moness, near Moness House Hotel. Burns kept dairy cattle – modern in his day, and would have noticed the prevalence of Highland Cattle in his tour of the West Highlands in 1787, although his literary works did not specifically feature the breed. Moness House today is part of a holiday complex of individual residences.

Urie House, Stonehaven, was never part of tourism. This 1905 or so photograph shows the building modified to the taste of the Baird family who purchased it in 1858. The presence of bull, cows and calves in the park suggests the Highland Cattle were not just for decorative purposes, however the Bairds were not as enthusiastic farmers as the previous Barclay Allardice owners. The house was last inhabited in 1943, owned by Timber Merchants in 1945, lost its roof in 1955 and is now in the hands of a development company.

The actual mist laden mountains of stirring tales and a source of gourmet beef was part of the attraction for intrepid Victorian and Edwardian tourists. They knew of the nourishing properties of beef tea to combat ill health, brought on by exposure to cold damp conditions, whether in cities or exploring northern Britain.

Right: **reproduced with kind permission of Unilever. Bovril is a registered Trademark of Unilever**. Mr J L Johnston, an émigré Scot in Canada, invented a nourishing beef-extract drink and returned to Britain to manufacture it in the 1870s. He named the product "Bovril" and the name was first registered as a trademark in 1886. Superb advertising for the product often used images of bulls. The wheeled toy in the advert is clearly of the highland breed. Other firms then developed similar convenient preparations of beef.

Below: **reproduced with kind permission of Boots Company Archives**. Jesse Boot of Nottingham developed a range of affordable healthcare products, one of which used beef-extract and was marketed as "Boots Fluid Beef". For his business achievements and wide ranging philanthropic services which included an active belief in making education accessible for all, Jesse Boot accepted the title of Lord Trent. His son read avidly about Scotland with a particular enthusiasm for the Highlands that led to years of successful Highland Cattle breeding in Ardnamurchan.

"Wherever did I put that BOVRIL!"

Boots Fluid Beef.

SUSTAINING AND NOURISHING

FOR INVALIDS AND TOURISTS.

PILLS POWDERS & REMEDIES

Reproduced with kind permission of The Times/News International Syndication Ltd.

Highland Cow

Tourists today are still charmed with the picturesque appearance of Highland cattle. Many excitedly seek a camera or postcard momento. Their photographs and postcards to friends have kept awareness of the breed fresh. A set of stamps paying tribute to British cattle breeds included this issue on 6 March 1984 commemorating the centenary of the Highland Cattle Society of Scotland. Mr Tom Copas, late of Cookham Dean, Berkshire, provided his champion cow Anna Bhuidhe of Glenforsa as a model for London illustrator Barry Driscoll's design. Her white bull calf had arrived by the time her fame took her to London for this photo call.

Watched by a red brindle, a yellow brindle leads the way in this painting by Peter Graham (1836 – 1921) of about fifty five highland bullocks on a drove route to market. Few artists include the black streaky coat of the brindle range. Graham depicts the innate dignity of the breed crossing a ford. He was held in high regard as a Scottish painter of Highland Cattle and their natural surroundings. His works however do not show brindle as clearly as the camera which captured one brindle cow with white socks in the picture opposite. Permission to reproduce an advertisment for the above work, owned privately, was kindly given by Nigel Stacy-Marks Ltd. Fine Paintings, specialists in paintings of Highland Cattle. Nigel and Ginny Stacy-Marks are enthusiastic owners of this aesthetically appealing breed.

This striking postcard scene of black, red, yellow and brindle Highland Cattle grazing in the Quiraing, Skye on a day of crisp light, probably about 1955 was published by the former J Arthur Dixon Studios. The unique basalt plateau, the Quiraing, is encircled by rocky formations, and proved a safe place to hold up to 4000 head of cattle when needs arose in the times when cattle changed hands more often by raiding forays than by negotiated sales. Note the brindle cow among the red, yellow and black.

courtesy of John Hinde UK. Ltd. for picture by J. Arthur Dixon

Aspects of Droving, Markets and Agricultural Shows

This remarkable photograph catches a Highland bullock leaping from the open ferry boat onto the shore at Glenelg during John Keay's 1981 drove from Skye to Crieff.

© Blair Urquhart

Drovers and Highland Cattle were an important part of Highland commerce for nearly 300 years. Walking cattle to a sales venue is common to pastoral peoples worldwide. Moving cattle from the Hebrides, Islands and Highlands to London and other expanding industrial cities during centuries of unparalleled turmoil and change is specific to Scotland. Drovers were men of awesome skills. To bring cash currency to their remote homelands they undertook large-scale movement of Highland Cattle on the hoof, known as a drove, to established markets being held on fixed dates hundreds of miles away. Physical strength and stamina, trustworthy reliability, commercial and political awareness, courage and a thorough knowledge of livestock were vital in this occupation, while a computer-like memory for unsignposted routes in 10 or 12 mile stages and a number-crunching mind for complex financial transactions would have been helpful.They had to ensure, that without travelling on a Sunday, the cattle would arrive at for instance Crieff, Falkirk, Carlisle, Norwich or London neither too early nor too late, nor too exhausted from the pace of the trek. Otherwise financial ruin would result. A single drove could number hundreds of animals (picture below only shows about 45) collected from many sources, and might occupy five continuous miles of the route. Reaching chosen destinations could take weeks or months of trekking. What powers of management strategy to control such a spread for so long without mobile phones or quad bikes! When a lightning flash might panic animals into bolting for miles without reaching a restricting hedge or dyke, when ill-health in the drove or the drovers might slow the pace, when thieves might scatter the drove to pilfer selected animals, when alternative routes had to be chosen either because of rivers in spate or areas in political turbulence (no advance warnings via radio reports in droving days), when in spite of such hazards the drovers delivered the cattle to market on time, negotiated a sale price in the foreign language of English and returned to distribute the earnings, it is no wonder the drover was held in high regard.

Canon Roderick Macleod of Macleod claimed the first man to take a drove of cattle from Skye to the mainland by swimming them across the narrows at either Kylerhea or Kyleakin was Donald MacIain Mhic Seumas of the clan Ranald in the early 17th century. That commercial initiative, whoever first took it, allowed vital trading that helped support highland communities for several generations. Highland Cattle became the 'must have' beef purchase to feed a rapidly expanding city populace. Writing in 1810 William Youatt noted that the first Englishman to visit the Hebrides to buy cattle was a Mr Moorhouse from Craven in Yorkshire with his purchase of six hundred from Mr Macleod of Waterside in 1763 and a deal with Mr Macdonald of Kingsburgh, Raasay for one thousand to be delivered free of expense to Falkirk. One thousand – and yes, complaints about difficulty accessing roads during droving seasons did arise. Youatt also reported hearsay that the Highland Cattle from Islay were the largest, those from Lewis provided the sweetest beef, and those from Skye were hardiest of all yet best able to improve with incredible rapidity on good pastures.

A HIGHLAND DROVE.

To supply the southern demand for beef and to remain marketable against the new bigger beef cattle becoming available, a trend began for increasing the size of the small Highland breed. A respected agriculturalist of these times, John MacNeill of Colonsay, was against "enlarging the breed rashly" as many had in his day, and have since, attempted. He liked "the ancient Hebridean type of West Highland Cattle with black long hair and close pile." He found that his two hundred calves per year gained size from feeding on grasses, turnips and potatoes and from less energy loss in winter by being housed. Science has proved that life forms can be specially bred to answer particular requirements but has yet to find an economically viable method of rearing very large bovines in the harsh conditions and meagre pasture of remote upland territories in Scotland. No doubt MacNeill would smile at the continued argument of whether 'artfully created big, or naturally small-but-suited-to-the-land' is the best way to meet the needs of the world populace. However he had no alternative to enlisting the help of drovers when it came to selling his annual crop of calves.

Selecting cattle for sale is no easy task. What if the very cow you choose to discard because she always throws bull calves produces, a year after the sale, the fine heifer you had needed!

Parting with a trusting 'character' was often tougher than is generally reported.

Above: On the road is a hungry cow accompanied by a crofter and a barefoot woman with a paraffin cannister. Possibly late 1920s.

> They walked in the lane together,
> The sky was covered in stars.
> They reached the gate in silence,
> He lifted down the bars.
> She neither smiled nor thanked him,
> Because she knew not how,
> For he was just the farmer's boy
> And she was a Highland cow.

(given by Cath Hunter, Kingussie, to the author from unknown source.)

Left: Herd boy looking after cows and calves circa 1908.

Above: When swimming their cattle across wide stretches of water, drovers organised them in groups of about ten. The cattle naturally swam in a close pack and suffered less accidental harm if free of ropes. This image of Loch Awe dates from around 1910.

Right: The construction of walls, hedges and fences created new difficulties on drove routes established long before such enclosures. These young Highland Cattle on the move to southern markets could not slake their thirst, cool their feet or browse as freely by the wayside as their forebears had.

In the Highlands.

Drovers wore knitted blue bonnets, rendered accurately by a few 19th century artists in their paintings of Highland life. (Right) George Rankin depicts assessing a bull at a tryst. Robert Burns mentions farmer Tam's "gude blue bonnet" in Tam O'Shanter, and a fashion conscious lad's "bonnet sae blue" in The Laddie's Dear Sel. In 1988 The Corries released their song The Bonnie Blue referring to blue bonnets worn by Highland clans defending their country. Blue dye, apparently difficult to reproduce repeatedly in identical hue, anciently was made in Europe from the woad plant. It was used both decoratively and medicinally by the Picts in tribal times, and imported by the ton to Leith and Dundee from commercial growers in England and France until the early 17th century. No evidence of woad cultivation in Highland Cattle breeding areas has yet come to my attention, although blue dye clearly featured in Highland woollen products. Drovers rich enough to return from London by boat to Leith could easily have purchased woad there to take north. In time the importations of indigo dye from India gained favour and production of woad ceased.

In October 1981 writer adventurer John Keay and team spread public awareness of Highland Cattle history with their challenging reconstruction of a 200 mile drove from the west of Skye to the former cattle market town of Crieff. As they discovered, controlling a drove of only 30 animals calls for a wide range of skills. It is fortunate that in the days of mass cattle movement on foot all droves were travelling in the same direction, otherwise spectacularly chaotic congestion would have occurred.

The news media followed his progress with interest, and John's book about the experience makes fascinating reading. A song in Gaelic from a real drover was given to John who printed an English version in his book Highland Drove. This verse tells how the drover recognised individual animals:

Photo: The late Jimmy Mitchell, Crieff

> "I've bought bullocks black and red,
> Known them by their ears and tails,
> Many weary days I've had
> On the long road to the sales."

One-directional travel, however, did not prevent bottleneck congestion at unavoidable parts of drove routes, usually at point of entry into stretches of water. Cattle numbers would swell as some droves waited for the right tide or favourable weather for the swim, while others kept arriving and joined the growing queue. One such place was Ardentrive (meaning promontary where cattle swim: aird an t'snaimh) on the island of Kerrera. Some 2000 sets of hooves shipped from Tiree, Coll, Mull, and parts of Morvern annually trekked over Kerrera and gathered at Ardentrive before swimming the sea strait to mainland Dunollie shore near Oban from where they would set off for southern markets. Another bottleneck at the south east of Skye was Kylerhea, notorious for the danger of the crossing to mainland Glenelg whichever tide was chosen for the plunge.

Here Highland Cattle at Arinagour, Coll, quietly await their turn to be hoisted aboard a small ferry boat for their journey to Mull, then to Oban market and unknown territory. " For 90 steerage passengers, when not occupied by cattle, animals, cargo or other encumbrances" was the message on a notice board on the MacBrayne's larger ship "Glencoe" in the 1920's.

Transporting cattle from the islands became easier though more expensive as steam ships came into ferrying use. Depending on island harbour facilities cows and bulls sometimes had to be hoisted individually on board in large sling contraptions. On occasion an animal slipped out of the sling or leapt overboard and swam back to the shore. Droves of Skye cattle no longer had to risk the dangerous kyles swim if the cost of shipping from the substantial Portree pier to Oban could be afforded. On arrival in Portree cattle were put in holding pens. "Then about 4am in the dark of autumn nights the barking of collie dogs could be heard moving the bellowing cattle to the pier for shipment to the mainland marts, the way through the village being lit by lanterns and flaming torches held by the drovers who shouted controls and rebukes in Gaelic to the collies, and compliments in best English. By 6am the paddle steamer manoeuvered out of Portree Harbour." (A A MacGregor)

There are shepherds today who scold their dogs in Gaelic, but not a drover will be found. Droving as a commercial enterprise ceased early in the 20th century, a casualty to progress. Sales prices had fluctuated unsustainably then plummeted terminally. Costs had increased with road toll charges per animal and heavy fines levied on drovers caught avoiding these roads. Charges were imposed for grazing at the stances (rest and grazing places) and for overnight stops there. Free grazing enroute was restricted by new dykes, hedges and later fencing. Ferries and steamships were expensive and proved not fast enough to deliver Scottish cattle to English markets before imported cattle had flooded them. By 1842 shipments from Scotland to Hull had ceased entirely because so many steamers from the continent brought in foreign cattle. New hornless, bigger and beefier cattle breeds were gaining favour at the same time as the quality of Highland beef was dropping as a result of forced clearance of crofters to very poor worthless land. Railway networks did improve transport time, but rail connections from London to Inverness, Oban and Kyle of Lochalsh, took so many years to construct that beef supplies for southern markets were lost to sources much cheaper than Scottish cattle, and frozen meat imports from New Zealand and Australia were impacting from 1877. Finally motor powered road haulage and the increase of motor cars on the roads made walking cattle even from one farm to another a hazardous event. Generations of drovers had adapted to momentous change as agricultural, industrial, educational, national, and transport developments reshaped everything, until finally their skills, their occupation and their goods were obsolete and redundant.

News and North British Agriculturist
VOL. CIX—JANUARY 1, 1957.
[REGISTERED AT THE GENERAL POST OFFICE AS A NEWSPAPER]

FARMING NEWS
AND NORTH BRITISH AGRICULTURIST

Courtesy of "The Scottish Farmer"

Two examples of the proximity of man and horned beast during transport to mainland markets. On page 34, the Highland Cattle on the pier in 1956 are being coaxed down a gangplank into a dark hold. The bull and two cows, on this page, leaving Kerrera in 1973 will not readily seek a dooking, particularly if they are with familiar people. But the unexpected emergence of a conning tower or blast of surround noise from a fighter jet on a low flying manoeuvre would startle even the most placid.

courtesy of the MacDougall family and House of Lochar

"These shaggy cows are such dears" wrote the sender of this postcard in 1935. These "dears" would not have had to swim to reach mainland markets as ferries had begun to ply the kyles from the 1820's. Now livestock travel to and from Skye by road in floats (livestock lorries). The breed name Highland Cattle dates from 1884, before which regional names were used including Black Cattle, Kylo, Skibo, Norlander, Scotch Highland, West Highlander. By the 1930s the term Kylo for Highland Cattle was scarcely heard. It may have derived from the pre-ferry practise of swimming sale cattle to mainland markets across sea narrows called Kyles from the Gaelic caol for sea-strait. Not all Highland Cattle reaching southern markets were from the islands so the term may have come from a gaelic word for high land pronounced as if Kaêl.

courtesy of Alastair White

Fairs, feills, trysts, and auction marts can all be called markets, but there are differences. Originally fairs were public occasions, officially authorised for the exchange of goods and produce of all sorts. Often held on festivals or holidays there might be entertainments along with refreshments to help the barter or buying and selling of diverse items from ribbons to livestock. The Martinmas Fair at Dunkeld was highly regarded for the quality of cattle included in the proceedings, as was the Dumbarton Muir Fair in June. Both fairs had ceased by the late 19th century when David Macrae from Oban gave this personal account of the cow fair held on Bruach-an-taillear plateau (Oban) in his childhood. There was a school holiday on the day and the place "was crowded with tents, and bellowing cattle, and sweetie stalls, and swarms of farmers, cattle dealers, and all sorts of people. Well, also, do I remember how, through that noisy chaos we wandered in unwearying and enchanted bewilderment, armed with little whips that we had prepared the night before, and which we waved and cracked at the more ferocious looking cows – always at a respectful distance." Provoking quiet animals into action seems an ever present temptation to the animal viewing public. Fairs persist today with various special attractions which often include displays of animals, jousting or falconry but no longer sales of livestock.

Making tea on a Uist fair. (Copyright.)

Feill, an old Gaelic name for markets of wide-ranging rural produce, lingered in usage and practice until the rise of auction marts took over the livestock exchange element of a feill.

Trysts as an established event may have developed *c.*1700 from arrangements to sell specifically cattle and sheep at a centralised location. Since everyone had to negotiate personally the sale of their livestock the word tryst was very appropriate, with its sense of privacy and trust about a mutually agreed meeting and the ensuing commitment made. Trysts, these specialised business venues for the cattle-droving industry, disappeared when commercially viable droving petered out around 1900. Drovers used to begin collecting cattle in May, adding more from lots of small markets through the summer as they progressed south to the major autumn trysts of Crieff, Falkirk, or Doune. If cattle had not been sold at August, September or October trysts the last chance in the year was at Doune Trysts held in November and commonly called Snowy Doune Fair. In action since at least the 1770s Doune was unusual for having free grazing, for up to a week before the sale, as late as 1845 by which time grazing charges were prevalent elsewhere. In 1893 The Scottish Farmer reported that Doune market had taken place in a slight fall of snow with a frosty cold wind, but was still attracting buyers from as far away as Wiltshire, Yorkshire, Alnwick, Wigtown, Castle Douglas and Dumfries. The cattle for purchase had come mainly from around Muir of Ord and Inverness. One dealer's lot of 237 animals were grazing in a wood in the neighbourhood of the tryst on the night of a bad storm, yet "notwithstanding the terrible destruction to trees – so much so that a great many of the cattle were so hemmed in by fallen timber that they had to be cut out of their peculiar position – not one of them was in the least injured." Four years after that however saw Doune attracting so few cattle and dealers that the market soon faded away. At the much larger Falkirk Tryst where vast gatherings of some 40,000 head of cattle were sold on, an awed agriculturalist wrote in the 1830's of his visit "In the latter part of the day when the tryst is over, to see every spot not only of the flat muir but of the beautifully undulating ground above, covered with cattle asleep and herdsmen in their characteristic Scottish dress either stretched in their plaids or resting for a while their wearied limbs – but still watchful" is truly unforgettable. The sheer scale of the Falkirk Tryst is very hard for 21st century people to envisage, and would test the special effect film techniques to simulate so many cattle, drovers, horses and dogs filling every space of several square miles. Continued expansion of both Falkirk and the Tryst caused a shift of the market location to the closeby village of Stenhousemuir without need to change the Tryst name. Falkirk Tryst closed finally in

"THE AULD FAIR O' DOUNE"

1901, but it is no surprise to find there is a Tryst Road in Stenhousemuir. Interesting though is the connection with Highland Cattle that a business operating from 44 Tryst Road has. Its founder was Andrew McCowan who had learned as a herdboy with the breed in Perthshire that their milk was particularly rich and creamy. In a career move to Stenhousemuir he created creamy Tablet in the 1920's, followed by Toffees and Fudge sold at inexpensive prices in wrappers bearing a picture of a Highland Cow. This trademark reflected the source of inspiration whereby McCowan sought to include nourishment in his confectionery. It also paid tribute to the remarkable event of the Falkirk Trysts which some of his older customers had attended. The Trysts became history but the McCowan products continue.

Livestock are now bought and sold by public auction in Auction Marts unless exchanged in private transactions on the farm, or after the auction. In this system sale cattle are presented for inspection and viewing in an area (auction ring) around which are gathered prospective buyers who at the invitation of an auctioneer bid the price they wish to offer to purchase the livestock 'under the hammer'. When competitive bids reach their peak the auctioneer closes that sale with a very audible rap on his desk, until which time the animals are said to be under the auctioneer's hammer. 'Mart' may come from that name for a mature bullock ready for slaughter in November to provide for winter tables. A link with the November festival of Martinmas is possible, however a dictionary suggests mart is of Dutch origin. The best known Mart these days for Highland Cattle, held under the auspices of the Highland Cattle Society, takes place in Oban twice a year. An Auction Mart there was first established in 1870 by the forward thinking Mr. Thomas Corson who located it conveniently close to where the railway station opened for business eleven years later. There was no breed society for Highland Cattle at that time. While Oban remains an excellent Mart location for cattle travelling from the Western Islands and Highlands it incurs fierce transport and

Highland Cattle on Colonsay about 1912 awaiting their boat journey to Jura, thence to mainland Keills, more markets and travel.

Private bargaining was replaced by public bidding for sales. Beasts as seen here at a sale by auction in Milton, South Uist, early 20 Century.

accommodation costs for the many Highland Cattle breeders in England and Wales loyal to their Society's choice of official sales venue. Angus Cameron, a farmer with droving experience seen opposite selling calves at Torlundy about 1920, innovated the Auction Mart at Fort William in 1890. He bought and sold many cattle at the market stance which is now Claggan village, and remembered the days when some 2000 might change hands there in the November fair. He handed on his auctioneer skills to his son Donald, well known Fort William farmer, whose writings and brief personal contact helped this author's researches. Of the late Donald's family who live in the area one has maintained a fold of Highland Cattle that would invoke a hearty compliment from his grandfather Angus were he to wander Glen Nevis today. The Auction Mart at Thainstone, Inverurie, serving the north east of

Scotland today deals with greater numbers of Continental and Continental Cross breeds than of Highland Cattle, the days when the Aberdeenshire strain of black Highland Cattle were plentiful having long since gone. But auctioneers and farmers at Dingwall and Thainstone were to prove as innovative as Corson and Cameron. They devised and operated the first ever 'virtual' auction system in Scotland using computers and television. Purchasers could bid on pictures of animals filmed on the farm instead of seeing them live in the auction ring. That temporary solution prevented the farming industry from grinding to a halt during the 1990's government restrictions on farm-animal movement enforced as part of disease control measures, but was an inadequate way to assess livestock. Outbreaks of cattle diseases in the Droving days simply shut down markets altogether.

courtesy of the Cameron family and The Highland Livestock Heritage Society archives.

Small local and huge national agricultural shows (ilustrated this page and opposite) are popular events with the general public. For many it is the closest they ever get to the farm livestock, produce, and rural skills, without which Britain could one day starve. Entertainments from sheep-dog displays to jousting, from heavy-horse carriage displays to pole-climbing by forestry workers, now run alongside competitions for champions among the livestock presented at that show. Static displays of the newest agricultural machinery, of floral art, and the latest in countryside management and fashion, complement a range of stalls with various sales items and edible delights. A variety of live music jollies the spirit of the day. The continued existence of Highland Cattle throughout Britain owes much to the generosity and dedication of those who, at no small personal cost, ensure the breed has a presence at all major agricultural shows. Because this hardy breed is found in uplands, moorlands, mountains and islands from the Isle of Wight to Foula, it often has further to travel to shows and markets than other breeds. New European transport regulations threaten the fragile viability of farming Highland Cattle in small folds in the territory it is best suited to. Consequently the numbers might fall seriously, again because of adverse market forces insurmountable by individual breeders in remote areas.

© UFC

© EJC

Shiploads of live foreign cattle unloaded at English ports introduced serious diseases to the British Isles. Foot and Mouth Disease first arrived in 1839, and was brought in again in 1892 leading to sporadic outbreaks ever since. Pleuro-pneumonia spread in 1844, and devastating Rinderpest in 1865. The remote habitat of Highland Cattle in uncontaminated hill grazings kept the breed largely free of these shocking episodes. When in 1986 an unknown cattle disease in English dairy cows spread like a plague, Highland Cattle remained predominantly free of it, because they were seldom fed the protein packed concentrate feeds for fast growth, common in British farming since the 1920s. Imported bone was processed as an ingredient in the concentrates some of which were found to transmit the new affliction Bovine Spongiform Encephalopathy (BSE). Although the British authorities effectively eradicated BSE they were unable to confirm the original source. The few exceptions to naturally fed Highlands most likely occurred when they had cleverly self-accessed concentrates from farm storage areas, or if a competitor's attempt to win some coveted show championship included giving these concentrates in the hope of producing the winning appearance in the animals on their one day in the show judging ring.

Agricultural Shows do nevertheless fulfil an important role providing information knowledge and understanding in an interactive forum, and opportunities for generating good business, in a venue full of entertainment and fun.

Amid the agricultural show ground spectacle and displays expected by today's public there would be much to astonish a herd lad from the 1860s, or indeed baffle: aircraft overhead, solar powered water spouts, exotic creatures. But he would find a safe zone with the familiarity of unchanged Highland Cattle.

By order of the Bailie of Regality a boy near Cromdale in 1700 was hanged for letting the cow he was herding stray into a cornfield. From quite a young age boys had to help with the livestock and the entire household worked on the harvesting. The traditional sharing of general work was arrested and the input from children keenly missed when compulsory education became law in 1872. Children lost opportunity to acquire land skills and their parents had to find money to hire labourers. This painting by Aberfeldy artist A. Scott Rankin (1868 – 1942) entitled The Herd, may have reminded teachers that in addition to schooling most rural children continued to have family duties which could include providing a regular meal of fish. In the Ayrshire tongue of Burn's time herd boys were called "guid boys".

Livestock farming, like all industries, has a range of specialist words. Some, like heifer, dam, bullock enjoy more general usage than others such as fold and dossan. Their meaning, leads to a wealth of information about Highland Cattle, and are introduced here through the fictional interactions of bi-lingual Donald McOran and his family from Strath Crodh between 1815 and 2005.

"Did you put them in the fold yet, Donald?" – a crofter, born in 1815, speaking to his young son in 1850.

In this picture, dating from 1913 or possibly slightly before, a fold of Highland Cattle pause for a photographer in Mull, a stronghold of the breed. A term exclusive to Highland Cattle, fold means herd. Highland Cattle breeders amicably uphold the convention of speaking about a fold rather than herd in tribute to past centuries of the breed's prominence in Scotland when the practice of enfolding (en-field-ing!) them in a safe enclosure, a fold, overnight was common. This gave some protection from predators and thieves in the times before hedges, dykes or fences enclosed land, whilst at the same time a natural manuring boost to the ground in the enclosure, usually "in-bye", meaning close to the farm or croft.

Black Highland cattle, once the norm, were rare by the 1950s entirely due to sustained selection of other colours, particularly red, by cattle owners over some hundred years. The late Mr Archie Howat, Rigg Farm, Kirkconnel dedicated years to encouraging the reappearance of the dormant black gene and by the 1990s had bred the bull in the lower left picture, astonishingly similar to the bull in the 1910 postcard above it.

A plain working bull with sparse dossan and bullocky horns like the fictitious "Craiganour"

This cow with profuse dossan listens with her left ear to her calf moving away while she assesses an approaching stranger. © UFC

"Donald, better check Craiganour. He lost most of his dossan on yonder pine stump an' I thought he was in good condition too. He'll be no use for the show now, but its maybe just as well, cos he's too high in the horn for a show bull tho' his calves are great. Busdubh's too close to calving, so if you must take a beast to this years show it'll have to be a yearling. Best ye get busy with the halter training and set a new fashion in leading round the ring." – same crofter in 1855 to same son, now 15 years old, applying himself to crofting skills.

The word dossan, exclusive to Highland Cattle, means the long forelock or fringe tumbling down the forehead, of both sexes. The dossan gives protection from flying pests and driving rain hail and snow. While the long outer hairs of the Highland's double coat are cast for summer the dossan remains all year, unless itched off due to pest infestation, or sparse from malnutrition. Thick long dossans can restrict vision to some degree, but this is compensated for by very keen hearing and sense of smell. If on approaching a Highland cow she seems to be looking elsewhere, one ear is almost certain to be angled in your direction monitoring your progress. Very long straight eyelashes give additional protection from the tough environment this breed evolved to withstand.

"Hamish, son, best ye put yer mind tae choosing a University course. The croft'll no support us all, an' the wee lass has a deal of growing yet." The crofter telling his younger son in 1860 that he'll need to leave to earn a living.

A croft is a parcel of land subject to a system of renting devised *c*.1800 by landowners seeking to force the cattle- rearing native populace to relocate along the coast. A crofter is the tenant of the croft. Despite access to shared common grazing, the croft is insufficient to sustain a family, the purpose being to make crofters work part time on the estates. A solution to the cascade of negative effects from over 150 years of uninformed exploitation of many Highland estates is emerging with new regulations on land use. Authorities now recognise the benefit of cattle on the hill and want to attract people into productive crofting. The word croft may be Anglo saxon or could derive from croit, gaelic for small enclosed field.

"Baravalla Dhu calved this morning. She's inbye, so you better check there's plenty water, an the mineral lick's there, an have a squint at the calfie. The vet's coming to see if our wanderer Ruthaig's in-calf. Tether her in the byre Donald, and just take the vet right there. I'll be another hour at the sheep fank. Off you go now boy." Boy Donald at 25 years old being given more responsibility on the croft in 1865.

Calved means gave birth to a calf. An in-calf i.e.pregnant, bovine achieves cow status after her first calving at 3 or 4 years of age in the Highland breed. A cow is termed dam in records of her calvings. Highland cows are renowned for their no fuss easy calving and good mothering.

"Which cow is the wee calf's dam, Daddy?" Catherine, Donald's wee daughter, grandchild to our crofter, on noticing a young calf down a bank of irises and rushes. Catherine was showing off her knowledge of farming talk as she accompanied her dad on his daily check of the cows in 1870. "Well now. Which do you think?" replied Donald gently inviting his wee lass to learn how to move safely among the beasts by reading their behaviour. Ears pulled back, agitated tail twitchings, a little snort with the raising of the head can indicate an animal is unsettled or disturbed.

"Donald d'you see yon red heifer that's not in calf? She's growing a bit bullocky.(Unfeminine) She's for the October sales. An' I think you should take along Maldag as well, an' hold out for a good price for her." Our 60yr old crofter talking to Donald about reducing the number of cows on the croft in 1875 with observant Catherine listening.

A heifer (quey or heifer stirk) is a female bovine, any breed, up to the time of her first calving. Highland heifers are well capable of having a "teenage pregnancy" even before they are a year old, but it can deplete the animal's future stamina, stunt her growth, or might cause a skipping cow ie. one who does not calf each year but skips one or a few between calvings and therefore does not earn her keep. Highland Cattle are best allowed their natural slow maturing, calving first at four years old, but the quicker cash flow from earlier calving fast growth Continental cattle breeds has helped to make Highland Cattle the minority breed it is today, even although the Highland cow will produce calves for years after other breeds have "retired".

The pure bred highland bull Sputnik of Benmore, calved in 2001. With thanks to the late John Taylor, Braes of Ardeonaig. © UFC

"Whose bull sired that hefty calf, then? It's a heifer too." Crofter Donald to his father after checking the cattle in 1880.

A bull is a mature male bovine, any breed, capable of procreating offspring and in that capacity called a sire in records of his progeny. The introduction of the croft system forced a reduction in the number of cattle any one crofter could keep. One bull per herd was no longer practical, there being no herd. The practice of sharing one bull in a crofting community had to develop, which brought problems of inbreeding, hence Donald's question. Until the 20th century many landowners seemed oblivious to the wider effects of mass felling of forests or of replacing hill cattle and Highland people with sheep and deer. The perceptive concerns of the few bonnet-lairds at their peers' land use went unheeded. Bonnet-lairds are resident landowners who work their own land, several of whom kept numbers of Highland Cattle through lean years when the breed was almost unmarketable.

"It would be grand if you could put the bullocks to the hill today, Hamish. Mind now, they might take off – they're a bit skittish – maybe a fox lurking." – Donald to university graduate brother Hamish, now a minister in Glasgow and visiting the home croft run by Donald. 1885.

A bullock (steer) is a neutered male bovine, any breed, incapable of siring any progeny. Only the best male calves are kept to become sires, the others are neutered by a vet, often also dehorned, and sold on as "store cattle" to commercial grazier beef producers. A young bullock is sometimes called Stirk or Stot, and when ready for sale a Mart. The word Ox, rarely used now for a bullock, survives in the trade name Oxo for a compressed powdered beef product, and also place names such as Oxford, Oxenford, and in plants such as the ox-eyed daisy and the ox tongue fern. Teams of oxen, that is bullocks, pulled ploughs and carts. They developed greater muscle mass and body bulk than bulls, and an amazing spread of horn longer and thicker than bull or cow horns. Crofters preferred their calm steadiness to the excitability of horses. They could be worked for up to seven hours before needing to stop to eat, but were slower in pace than horses. Even without the body building result of haulage work bullocks do grow larger than bulls, ultimately providing a greater amount of butcher meat. Beef from bulls is not generally consumed in Britain but some countries favour it.

Pure bred highland bull Lasgair of Millerston. © T.McLatchie

51

"Keep Bellag away from the Byre – she's learned to lift the latch to the grain store and see if you can put half a hay bale to MacGilleman. He's in–bye just now." Donald in 1890 to fourth child Dougie, keen to be a crofter like his grandfather.

Horns are a noticeable breed characteristic, with Highland bulls, cows and bullocks all naturally having horns. Even the tousled haired calves have sharp little points sprouting in the midst of their young dossans – an unexpected bump against you from these cute'n'cuddly babes can leave an entirely unplanned bruise. A close look at Highland cattle reveals there are rarely identical heads of horns. To the practised eye when all that's visible over a hillock, through furze in deep bracken or in a gully is the crowning glory, it is enough to identify the individual.

© UFC

The older the bull, cow or steer the larger its horns, for the horns grow continuously. A rich blood supply from a hollow core enables the horns to grow, makes them warm to the touch, sensitive to any whack on them, capable of precision contacts with the pointed tip such as scratching the itch place or opening a door, and capable of bleeding if accidentally broken, or if sandpapered too vigorously before being oiled shiny for that smooth photo-call look at Agricultural Shows. Shapely symmetric horns, carried with such seeming dignity, draw crowd admiration at every public appearance.

"No, Dougie, I'll not sell old Loppie. Gives me grand calves. Grandad said she would – an' she was the last wee calf he saw. Sweetest nature in the fold too. Must've had a knock when she was a calfie, to make that horn twist down. Now if she threw calves with bad horns – well that'd be different." Experienced Crofter Donald to impatient apprentice crofter son Dougie, in 1900.(threw meaning produced or gave birth to)

Lop-horns are uneven horns. Severe frost, poor diet, or heavy impact when young perhaps from a cow or horse kick or being tumbled to the ground by roping rodeo-style, can damage horn growth, often not evident for up to two years. Lop-horns can also be inherited. Occasionally over-zealous agricultural show competitors have tried to alter offending horn growth with heat treatments or weights but without lasting success.

"D'you see the plain horns, the thick heavy neck, and the tassle mid-belly Mam, well that's the bull d'you see. No ring in his nose he's that quiet." Elderly Donald with crofter son Dougie at his side speaking to a concerned new neighbour retired from the city who, wanting to cycle through the common grazings, had asked if there was a bull among the cattle. 1910.

© T. McLatchie

Good Highland bull horns come level out of the head, curve slightly forward with a slight rise to the points, and are thicker in girth at the base than cow horns. They are shorter than cow and steer horns. Unlike many hornless breeds Highland bulls seldom need to have a permanent nose ring because their disposition to humans is generally non-aggressive and quiet. A temporary nose-ring called a humbug is usually clipped in place when bulls are being manoeuvered in unpredictable circumstances such as being led through a public area or during agricultural shows, and for convenience some breeders do insert a permanent ring. But since many Highland bulls have no nose ring, apply the advice our Donald gave to his new neighbour if a need to identify a bull among livestock arises.

" No Mrs Pencarrington, its not maybe the best idea actually to give them, well for anyone to give them, scones on your way through. They get too eager, y'see. Might crowd round too close, nudging for more, when you've none. Could be a lot of horns around, just looking for more treats. Robina'll take you through the beasts if you like, then they'll know you and your bike and wont be bothered. They're never too keen on dogs though, if you're ever thinking of getting one? But they'll hardly throw a second look once they know yourself. Take a stick with you if you're worried." (beasts is a general term for farm livestock) Crofter Dougie in 1960, now himself elderly with his daughter Robina running the croft, being patiently helpful again to another new neighbour from the south, who has worries about Highland Cattle grazing across a moorland public right-of-way similar to public areas in the New Forest, England, where a variety of cattle breeds and ponies roam free.

Longer than bull horns and of greater variety in shape, Highland cow horns start level out of the head before rising upwards. The elegance of the up and backwards swirling shape is hard to equal, but the other main type where the horns spread wide in an upwards curve is also dramatically stylish. Once a Highland Cow has received a tap on the horns from a stick she will in future take note of any stick being handled and avoid her horns getting too close.

© T. McLatchie

Out of the mist came the fine Highland matrons hoping for tasty delights. © UFC

A pointed reminder for an artist.

"... what about their horns you say. Not a problem. There's no doubt they're a quiet breed when properly managed. They've an ancient shared existence with man, to whom they're not instinctively aggressive. But yes, I will concede, that, like anybody armed with weaponry the potential for injury is there. The only likely trigger for dangerous behaviour in this breed is when a cow with her calf thinks she has to defend it. My father and grandfather before him worked this croft all their days and never heard tell of a horning in the glen. The cardinal rule is never go between a cow and her calf. This sounds simple but you have to remember that Highland cows will hide their calf in clumps of rushes or a dip in the land or river bank, where it lies unseen quietly awaiting her return. This can be a distance from where the cow is grazing. So its wise to look well beyond the cows in the calving season if you find your route leads through their territory. Any more questions...?" Dougie addressing a gathering of 20th century agriculturalists visiting his traditionally managed fold in 1965, respectful of his 84 years of crofting life, and interested in his system of land and livestock management.

Horn use in this breed is normally for individual grooming, maintaining orderly ranking in access to feed-lots or the best chewing-the-cud spot, protection of calves from birth to weaning and, with bulls, also for the defence of their grazing space against an intruding bull – threatening posturing may take place between two bulls in the same field or one might simply remove the newcomer by tossing him over the fencing, but serious goring is virtually unknown and if it happened might derive from inexperienced management. Putting several bulls together in show rings tests the skill of the handlers in gaining co-operation from powerful animals imbued with a territorial instinct to establish dominance in their own space. Bulls quietly parading shoulder to shoulder with other bulls in a confined area deserve due credit for compliant behaviour during an unnatural experience.

© T. McLatchie

"... After their horns the next thing you notice is their thick hairy coat. Most people think that all Highland Cattle are a sort of toy teddy-bear colour. Well all these are pure bred pedigree Highlands." Crofter Robina addressing a group of 21st century tourists visiting the Highland fold inherited from her father Dougie, who had learned all about these cattle and their forebears in Mull, Lewis, Athole, and Applecross from his father Donald, son of the crofter born in 1815 and the great-grandfather of Robina.

The coat of Highland Cattle has two layers. The thick outer coat of long coarse hair sheds rain and snow and traps air for added insulation of the dense soft fleecy undercoat that maintains the body heat. The shaggy coated appearance is at its best in winter, but even when the outer coat has been cast for summer the dossan remains. The long outer coat can be flowing, wavy, straight or curled. Add to these variations the range of different coat colours and clearly the breed embraces a collection of individuals.

The whole-coat colours officially range from white through dun, yellow, red, brindle, to black. Here "through" means there can be pale to dark versions of each colour except black. Where patches of white occur in a pedigree animal the coat is called parti-colour. Coat colour is not of commercial significance in this breed. Old cattle lore however maintained that black coats were the toughest animals, that dun coats had the shortest outer coats, that white coats were the softest animals and that red, while less hardy than the black, were better at laying on quality beef quicker than any of the other colours.

© T. McLatchie

It would be easy for the unwary to miss the calf in this field

"They used to be a multi-purpose animal, Niall. Why d'you say it could never work to make fudge and cheese exclusively from creamy Highland milk –y'know, for this niche market people speak about."

"Quantity, lass. Quantity and constant supply" was Niall's opinion. Elderly Crofter Robina to her retired Beef Producer brother Niall in 2005.

Highland Cattle are a beef breed which yield low-fat meat of low cholesterol level but rich in protein, iron and flavour, when naturally reared in the traditional slow maturing way. There are subtle differences in flavour according to the predominant plants grazed. Areas with a prevalence of particular plants are, heather moorland, Hebridean machairs, wetlands grasses, birchwood and juniper outcrops. The term beef breed came into usage in the 18th century when domestic cattle - source of traction-power, food, leather, tallow for candles and cruisie-lamps before electricity lit people's homes, horn and bone artefacts, and natural fertiliser - were streamlined by selective breeding into two categories of cattle:- dairy for milk and beef for meat. Beef breed cows have ample milk for their own calf but not the extra yield that dairy cows, bred specially for that purpose since the 1780s, now provide for mass production of milk foodstuffs like cheese, yoghurt, cream, dried milk, custard and chocolate. There are not enough Highland Cattle in Britain, let alone Scotland, to yield the constant quantity of beef the supermarkets demand, and certainly not enough to supply a continuous production line in exclusively Highland-milk luxury foods for twelve months in the year. Traditional seasonality of food supplies is no longer a normal condition of life in Europe, but as Highland Cattle are very traditional "Long may they remain natural" say I. In 2004 Government statistics recorded a U.K.overall total of 2,903,366 cattle calves (all breeds) of which just 5,664 were Highland calves.

Generally when beef cattle are fed on rich pastures they naturally lay on extra fat which can be taken from the carcass and rendered into tallow. A biofuel derived from tallow was developed and put to use in the 1990s successfully powering electricity generating plants with less toxic emissions than oil power and yielding almost the same energy levels. This additional environment friendly potential in beef cattle is probably less widely known than the fact that the name for the popular hot dog snack is derived from the cowboy word "dogie" for a calf in the cattle ranching states of America. Cattle most favoured in the future might be specially bred at the instigation of a 'gwipo' – global-warming prevention officer, to process their day's browsing with minimal gaseous emissions, otherwise known as methane or digestive wind. How Highland Cattle might rate in a statistical report on this by-product of ruminants' conversion of herbage to meat and milk awaits a civil service project no doubt!

© UFC

Highland cows rearing calves on rough marshy grazing shared with heifers.